TAKE THE LEAD

TRUMPET

Bumper Book

Editorial, production and recording: Artemis Music Limited (www.artemismusic.com) • Published 2005

© 2005 by International Music Publications Ltd
First published by International Music Publications Ltd in 2005
International Music Publications Ltd is a Faber Music company
3 Queen Square, London WC1N 3AU

All rights reserved
Printed in England by Caligraving Ltd

Angels

Words and Music by Robert Williams
and Guy Chambers

Demonstration: CD1
Backing: CD2

Rather slow

Blueberry Hill

Words and Music by Al Lewis,
Vincent Rose and Larry Stock

Demonstration: CD1
Backing: CD2

Careless Whisper

Words and Music by George Michael
and Andrew Ridgeley

Demonstration: CD1
Backing: CD2

Come Away With Me

Words and Music by Norah Jones

Demonstration: CD1
Backing: CD2

Dance Of The Sugar Plum Fairy

Music by Pyotr Ilych Tchaikovsky

Demonstration: CD1
Backing: CD2

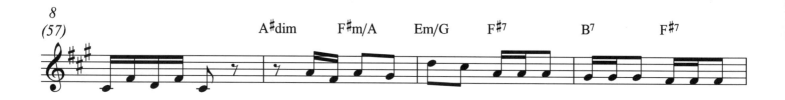

30
(79)

35
(84)

cresc.

39
(88)

42
(91)

46
(95)

50
(99)

Everybody Needs Somebody To Love

Words and Music by Bert Burns,
Solomon Burke and Jerry Wexler

Demonstration: CD1
Backing: CD2

Fascinating Rhythm

Music and Lyrics by George Gershwin
and Ira Gershwin

Demonstration: CD1
Backing: CD2

Guantanamera

Words and Music by Diaz Fernandez

Demonstration: CD1
Backing: CD2

I'll Be There For You

Words and Music by
Phil Solem, Marta Kauffman, David Crane,
Michael Skloff, Allee Willis and Danny Wilde

Demonstration: CD1
Backing: CD2

La Bamba

Traditional
Arranged by Ritchie Valens

Demonstration: CD1
Backing: CD2

In The Mood

Words by Andy Razaf
Music by Joe Garland

Demonstration: CD1
Backing: CD2

My Heart Will Go On

Words by Will Jennings
Music by James Horner

Demonstration: CD1
Backing: CD2

Over The Rainbow

Words by E Y Harburg
Music by Harold Arlen

Demonstration: CD1
Backing: CD2

Ballad tempo

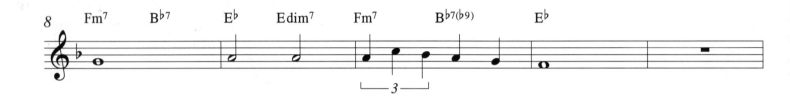

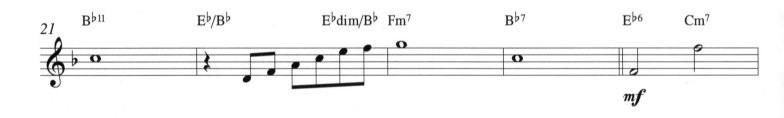

Singin' In The Rain

Words by Arthur Freed
Music by Nacio Herb Brown

Demonstration: CD1
Backing: CD2

Medium swing

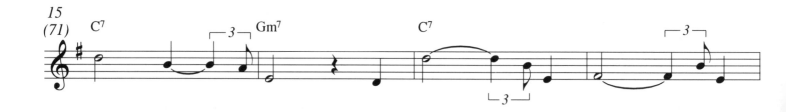

Sound Of The Underground

Words and Music by Brian Higgins,
Niara Scarlett and Miranda Cooper

Demonstration: CD1
Backing: CD2

Star Wars (Main Theme)

Music by John Williams

Demonstration: CD1
Backing: CD2

Summer Nights

Words and Music by Jim Jacobs
and Warren Casey

Demonstration: CD1
Backing: CD2

Summertime

(From *Porgy And Bess*®)

Demonstration: CD1
Backing: CD2

Music and Lyrics by George Gershwin,
Du Bose Heyward, Dorothy Heyward
and Ira Gershwin

Uptown Girl

Words and Music by Billy Joel

Demonstration: CD1
Backing: CD2

Moderate rock & roll

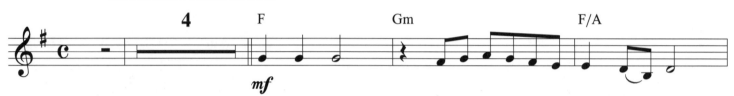

© 1983 Joelsongs, USA
EMI Songs Ltd, London WC2H 0QY

When You Say Nothing At All

Words and Music by Paul Overstreet
and Don Schlitz